Paper Folding for the Mathematics Class

Donovan A. Johnson

University of Minnesota
Minneapolis, Minnesota

NATIONAL COUNCIL OF TEACHERS OF MATHEMATICS
1201 Sixteenth Street, N. W.
Washington, D. C. 20036

Copyright © 1957 by

The National Council of Teachers of Mathematics, Inc.
1906 Association Drive, Reston, Virginia 20191-1593
All rights reserved

Fourteenth printing 1999

ISBN 0-87353-412-3

Printed in the United States of America

Introduction

As a successful, dynamic teacher of mathematics you are constantly looking for ways to build understandings, interests, and attitudes. An intriguing way of adding realism and interest to your mathematics teaching is to fold paper. Forming straight lines by folding creases on a sheet of paper is a simple way of illustrating and discovering relationships of lines and angles. After a relationship has been found by folding paper, formal statements about it no longer seem strange and difficult. Thus, paper folding not only simplifies learning mathematics, it also builds understandings and appreciation.

The exercises suggested in this publication have application at many levels of instruction. Most of the introductory constructions are appropriate for junior high school pupils. Other sections, such as the material on conics, are adapted to the superior or advanced student. Many of the topics, for example hexaflexagons, are enrichment activities of a recreational type. Many of the folding exercises may be a basis for laboratory work in a geometry class. Select the projects that you think will make a unique contribution toward better learning in your classroom.

The only materials you need for paper-folding exercises are a sheet of paper and a pencil. Although any paper is usable, heavy wax paper is most suitable. On wax paper a crease becomes a distinct white line, and its transparency simplifies superposition. Some students have found tracing paper a suitable material because of the ease of writing on it. By folding, lines and points are made coincident by placing one upon the other.

Although paper folding is easy, it is not always easy to give clear instructions to students orally or in writing. It is always helpful to have directions and diagrams to supplement demonstrations. As you read the descriptions below, try them out by performing the folding described. After you have practiced these, it is likely that you can extend the method to many more complex constructions.

In mathematics we always make certain basic assumptions on which we build a mathematical structure. In paper folding we assume the following postulates:

- Paper can be folded so that the crease formed is a straight line.
- Paper can be folded so that the crease passes through one or two given points.
- Paper can be folded so that a point can be superimposed on another point on the same sheet.
- Paper can be folded so that a point on the paper can be superimposed on a line on the same sheet and the resulting crease pass through a second given point.

- Paper can be folded so that a straight line can be superimposed on another straight line on the same sheet.
- Lines and angles are said to be equal if they coincide when one can be superimposed upon another by folding the paper.

If these assumptions are accepted, then it is possible to perform all the constructions of plane Euclidean geometry by folding and creasing.

Patterns for folding a great variety of polyhedra will be found in the following publications:

HARTLEY, MILES C. *Patterns of Polyhedrons*. Chicago: The author, University of Illinois, 1945.

CUNDY, H. M. and ROLLETT, A. P. *Mathematical Models*. London: Oxford University Press, 1952.

The writer wishes to give credit to those who have previously described many of the paper-folding projects explained above. The writer is most indebted to Robert C. Yates who furnished the original inspiration and information for using these materials.

References on paper folding:

BERGER, EMIL; JOSEPH, MARGARET; SAUPE, ETHEL; and UTH, CARL. "Devices for the Mathematics Laboratory." *The Mathematics Teacher* 44:247-49; 48:42-44, 247, 49.

LEEMING, JOSEPH. *Fun with Paper*. Philadelphia: J. P. Lippincott Co., 1939.

ROW, SUNDARA. *Geometric Exercises in Paper Folding*. Chicago: The Open Court Publishing Co., 1941.

YATES, ROBERT C. *Geometrical Tools*. St. Louis: Educational Publishers, 1949.

All figures for this manuscript were drawn by Charles B. Bastis, University High School, Minneapolis, Minnesota.

How To Fold the Basic Constructions

A variety of geometric figures and relationships can be demonstrated by following the directions below. If you have a supply of wax paper, we are all set for a new way of learning mathematics.

1. Folding a straight line

Any point P of one portion of the sheet of paper is folded over and held coincident with any point Q of the other portion. While these points are held together tightly by the thumb and a finger of one hand, the fold is creased with the thumb and a finger of the other hand. This crease forms at points equidistant from P and Q. The crease is extended by holding the crease tightly with the thumb and finger of both hands, then pulling the hands apart. The tension used in completing the crease should be kept constant on both surfaces. Thus the distance from points P and Q to the crease remains equal on each portion of the sheet. The crease formed is then the locus of all points of the sheet which are equidistant from P and Q. Is this locus a straight line?

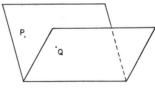

Figure 1

2. A straight line through a given point

Fold the sheet over with the given point on the outside. Carefully form a short crease that passes through the point. Extend the crease as described above.

3. A line perpendicular to a given straight line

Fold the sheet over so that a segment of the given line AB is folded over on itself. Hold the lines together tightly with the thumb and finger of both hands. Form the crease by pulling the hands apart with the right thumb and finger sliding. Why is the straight angle formed by the given line AB bisected by the crease CD?

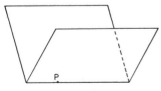

Figure 2

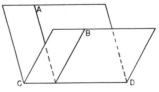

Figure 3

1

4. The perpendicular to a line at a point on the line

Fold the paper so the given line AB is superimposed on itself as in Number 3 above and so that the crease passes through the given point P.

Fold B on A but before creasing slide the paper, keeping the line coincident with itself, until the crease will pass through the given point P. Why is the fold through P perpendicular to AB?

5. A line perpendicular to a given line and passing through a given point P not on the line

This construction uses the same method of folding as Number 4 above.

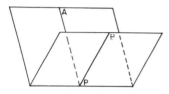

Figure 4

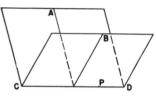

Figure 5

6. The perpendicular bisector of a given line segment

Fold the paper so that the end points of the given line AB are superimposed on each other. Why is this crease CD the perpendicular bisector of AB? Locate any point on the perpendicular bisector. Test by superposition to see if this point is equally distant from A and B.

7. A line parallel to a given straight line

First fold the perpendicular EF to the given line AB as in Number 3. Next fold a perpendicular to EF. Why is this last crease CD parallel to the given line AB?

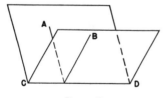

Figure 6

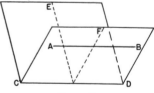

Figure 7

8. A line through a given point and parallel to a given straight line

First fold a line CD through the given point P perpendicular to the given line AB as in Number 5. In a similar way fold a line EF through the given point *P* and perpendicular to the crease *CD* formed by the first fold. Why does this crease provide the required line?

9. The bisector of a given angle

Fold the paper so that the terminal sides *AC* and *BC* of the given angle *ACB* coincide. Why does the crease pass through the vertex and divide the given angle into two equal angles?

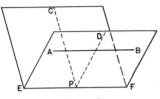

Figure 8

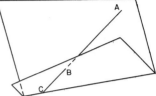

Figure 9

10. The location of equally spaced points along a line CD

Establish any convenient length as the unit length by folding a segment of the line upon itself. Form several equal and parallel folds by folding back and forth and creasing to form folds similar to those of an accordion.

11. The formation of a right angle

Take any piece of paper, one edge (*b* x *c*) of which must be straight as in Figure 11A below. Fold one end down at an acute angle as shown in Figure 11B. Then fold *b* over to touch *c*, making Figure 11C. Why is the angle *YXZ* a right angle?

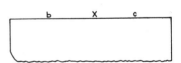

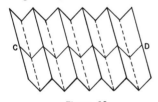

Figure 10

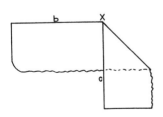

Figure 11A

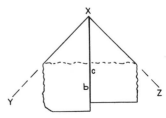

Figure 11B

Figure 11C

3

Geometric Concepts
Illustrated by Paper Folding

12. Vertical angles

Fold any two intersecting creases AB and CD intersecting at O. Compare the vertical angles by folding through the vertex O, placing BO on CO. Do AO and DO coincide? Are vertical angles equal?

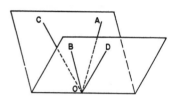

Figure 12

13. The sum of the angles of a triangle

(a) Fold the altitude BD of the given triangle ABC (Figure 13A).

(b) Fold the vertex of the triangle B upon the base of the altitude D (Figure 13B).

(c) Fold the base angle vertices A and C to the base of the altitude D. Does $\angle A + \angle B + \angle C$ make up a straight angle (Figure 13C)?

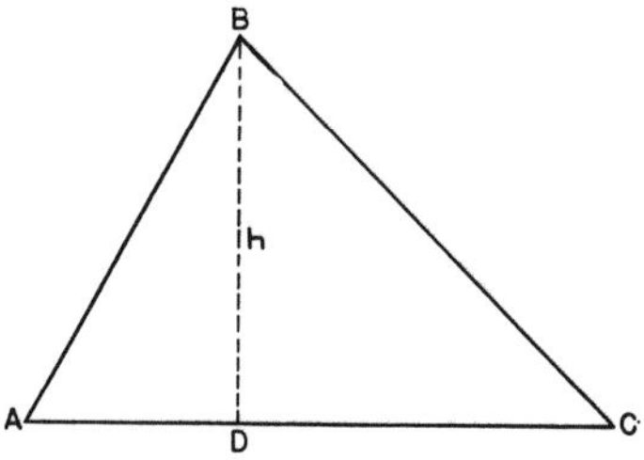

Figure 13A

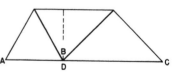

Figure 13B

14. The area of a triangle

In Figure 13C the rectangular shape has sides equal to one-half the base of triangle ABC and one-half the altitude BD (Figure 14). What is the area of the rectangle? How does the area of the original triangle ABC compare with this rectangle? What then is the area of the triangle?

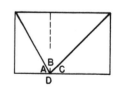

Figure 13C

15. The midpoint of the hypotenuse of a right triangle

(a) Fold or draw any right triangle ABC (Figure 15A).

(b) Bisect the hypotenuse AB by folding A on B. Fold the line from the midpoint D to C (Figure 15B).

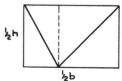

Figure 14

4

(c) Compare CD, AD, and BD by folding a crease through D. Will CD and BD coincide? Fold another crease through D to see if CD and AD will coincide. Is $CD = AD = BD$?

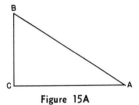

Figure 15A

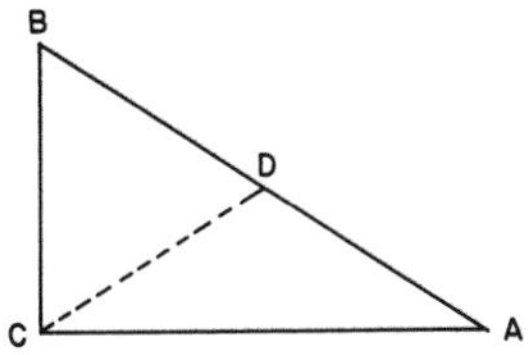

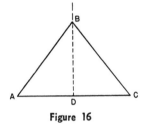

Figure 15B

16. The base angles of an isosceles triangle

Fold the perpendicular bisector BD of a given line segment AC. Crease oblique lines AB and BC from the ends of the given line to a common point B on the perpendicular bisector to form an isosceles triangle ABC. Compare the base angles by superposition by folding along BD. Are angles A and C equal?

Figure 16

17. The intersection of the altitudes of a triangle

Fold the altitudes to each side of the given triangle. Do they intersect in a common point? What is the intersection point of two altitudes called? How do the distances from the point of intersection of these altitudes to the vertices and the bases of the triangle compare?

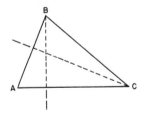

Figure 17

18. The intersection of the angle bisectors of a triangle

Fold the bisectors of each angle of the given triangle. Do the bisectors intersect in a common point? What is the point of intersection of two angle bisectors called? Fold the perpendicular from this point of intersection of two angle bisectors to each side of the triangle. Compare the lengths of these perpendiculars by superposition. Are the lengths equal?

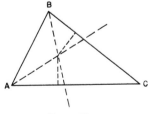

Figure 18

5

19. The intersection of the perpendicular bisectors of the sides of a triangle

Fold the perpendicular bisectors of each side of the given acute triangle. What is the common point of intersection of these lines called? Fold creases from this point to each vertex of the triangle. Compare these lengths by superposition. Are these lengths equal?

20. The intersection of the medians of a triangle

Bisect the three sides of the given triangle. Fold the crease from the midpoint of each side to the opposite vertex. What is this common point of intersection called? How do the distances from the point of intersection of two medians to each vertex of the triangle compare? Try balancing the triangle by placing it on a pin at the intersection of two medians. What is this point called?

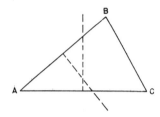

Figure 19

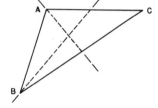

Figure 20

21. The area of a parallelogram

Cut a trapezoid with one side CB perpendicular to the parallel sides. Fold the altitude DE. Fold CF parallel to AD. When triangle FCB is folded back, $ADCF$ is a parallelogram. When triangle ADE is folded back, $DCBE$ is a rectangle. Are triangles ADE and FCB congruent? Is rectangle $BCDE$ equal to parallelogram $ADCF$? What is the formula for the area of a parallelogram?

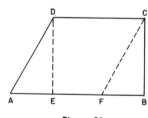

Figure 21

22. The square on the hypotenuse is equal to the sum of the squares on the two other legs of a right triangle

Use a given square $ABCD$. Make any crease GH. Complete the square $GHEF$ by forming right angles at G and H. Fold GJ, HK, EL, and FM by folds perpendic-

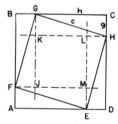

Figure 22

6

ular to the sides of the given square $ABCD$. Note that $LH = GK = FJ = AF$. How can you prove that $h^2 + g^2 = c^2$?

23. The diagonals of a parallelogram

Fold the diagonals of a given parallelogram. Compare the lengths of intersected segments by superposition. Are the diagonals of a parallelogram equal? Do the diagonals bisect each other?

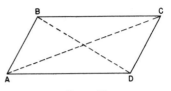

Figure 23

24. The median of a trapezoid

Fold the altitudes at both ends of the shorter base CI and DJ of the trapezoid $ABCD$. Bisect each nonparallel side and connect these midpoints with a crease EF. Does this median EF bisect the altitudes? Is this median EF perpendicular to the altitudes? Is this median parallel to the bases? Fold A on I and B on J. How does the sum of CD and AB compare with the median EF?

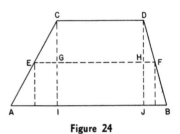

Figure 24

25. The diagonals of a rhombus

Fold the diagonals of a given rhombus $ABDC$. Compare angles and lengths of the diagonals by superposition. Do the diagonals intersect at right angles? Do the diagonals bisect each other? Is triangle ABC congruent to triangle BCD? What area will be found by the product of AD and CB?

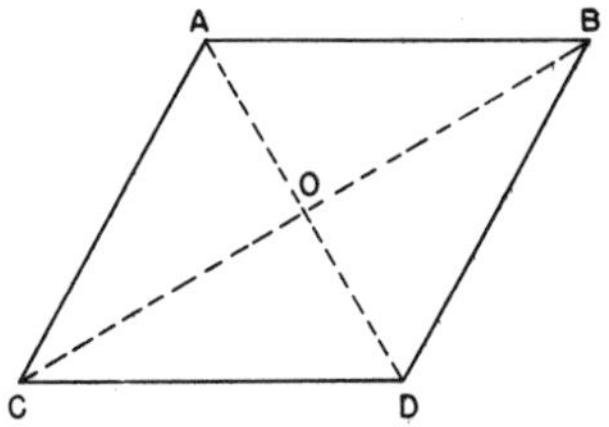

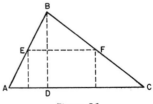

Figure 25

26. A line midway between the base and vertex of a triangle bisects the altitude and equals one-half the length of the base

Bisect two sides of the triangle ABC. Fold a crease through these mid-points EF. Fold the altitude to the side which is not bisected. Is EF the perpendicular bisector of BD? Is EF parallel to AC? Fold A and C upon D. How does the length of EF compare with the length of AC?

Figure 26

7

Circle Relationships
Shown by Paper Folding

Cut out several large circles. Some of them should be drawn with a pattern so that the center is not located.

27. The diameter of a circle

Fold the circle upon itself (Figure 27). Does the crease AB bisect the circle? What line is the crease AB?

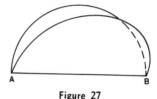

Figure 27

28. The center of a circle

Fold two mutually perpendicular diameters. Are the diameters bisected? At what point do the diameters intersect?

29. The center of a circle of which only a portion (which includes the center) is available

Fold any two chords AB and CD. Fold the perpendicular bisectors of these chords. Why is the intersection M of these perpendicular bisectors the center of the circle?

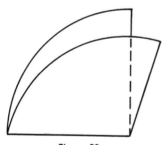

Figure 28

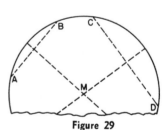

Figure 29

30. Equal chords and equal arcs in the same circle

Locate the center O of the circle by folding two diameters. Fold the circle along a diameter AD. While folded, fold a portion of the circle forming two equal chords, AB and AC. How do the arcs AB and AC compare? Fold radii BO and CO to form the

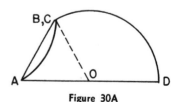

Figure 30A

8

central angles *AOB* and *AOC*. Compare the central angles by superposition. Fold the perpendicular bisector *EO* and *FO* of chords *AB* and *AC*. Compare lengths *EO* and *FO* by superposition. What generalizations can you state about equal chords and equal arcs of the same circle?

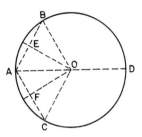

Figure 30B

31. A diameter perpendicular to a chord

Fold any chord *AB*. Fold a diameter *CD* perpendicular to this chord. How do the segments of the given chord *AE* and *EB* and the subtended arcs *AC* and *CB* compare?

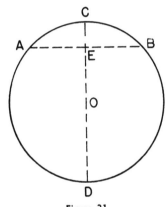

Figure 31

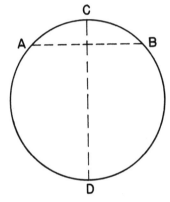

Figure 32

32. The perpendicular bisector of a chord

Fold any chord *AB* and its perpendicular bisector *CD*. Fold two diameters, neither one parallel to the perpendicular bisector. Do the three creases intersect in a common point? What is the point of intersection of the perpendicular bisector and one diameter called?

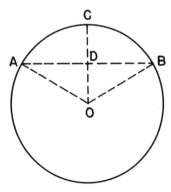

Figure 33

33. A radius that bisects the angle between two radii

Fold any two radii *AO* and *BO*. Fold

9

the chord AB subtended by these radii. Fold the bisector OC of the angle between the radii, AO and BO. How is the bisector of angle AOB related to the chord AB?

Exercises 34, 35, and 36 below should be done with a circle outlined on a sheet of wax paper.

34. Arcs of a circle intercepted by parallel lines

Fold any diameter AB of circle O. Fold two parallel chords by folding two perpendiculars to this diameter. Compare the intercepted arcs CD and EF by folding the parallel lines upon each other so that the intercepted arcs coincide. How do the lengths of arcs ED and EF compare?

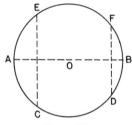

Figure 34

35. The angle inscribed in a semicircle

Fold any diameter AB. At one end of the diameter fold any chord AC. Fold the crease CB forming a triangle ABC. What is the size of the angle formed by the chords AC and BC?

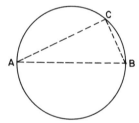

Figure 35

36. To construct a tangent to a circle at a given point on the circle

Fold the diameter of the given circle passing through the given point P on the circle. At P fold the line perpendicular to the diameter. Why is this last crease a tangent to the circle?

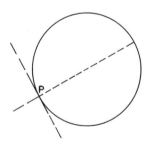

Figure 36

Products and Factors

37. $(x+y)(x-y)=x^2-y^2$

(a) Let any rectangular sheet of paper represent a rectangle with dimensions x and $x + y$ (Figure 37A).

(b) To determine y, fold the upper left-hand vertex down to the bottom edge. Thus $x = RT$ and $y = UZ$. Fold along VU (Figure 37B).

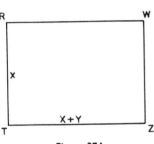

Figure 37A

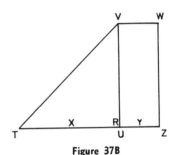

Figure 37B

(c) Return R to its original position. $RTVU$ is a square x units on each side. $UVWZ$ is a rectangle with dimensions x and y (Figure 37C).

(d) Fold W to line VU forming a right triangle VWS. Fold LS (Figure 37D).

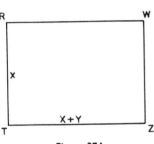

Figure 37C

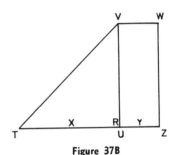

Figure 37D

11

(e) Label the dimensions of each section as shown in Figure 37E. Cut or tear into the rectangles M, N, P, and Q. Discard rectangle M.

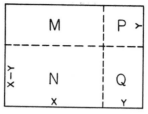

Figure 37E

(f) Rectangles N and Q will form a rectangle with the dimensions $(x + y)$ and $(x - y)$ in Figure 37F. The area of N is $x(x - y)$ or $x^2 - xy$. The area of Q is $y(x - y)$ or $xy - y^2$. Thus $(x + y) (x - y)$ $= (x^2 - xy) + (xy - y^2) = x^2 - y^2$.

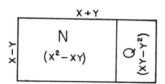

Figure 37F

(g) Use rectangles N, Q, and P to form the square x by x (Figure 37G). By removing P (subtracting y^2), the resulting figure can be formed into the rectangle $(x - y) (x + y)$. Thus $x^2 - y^2 = (x - y) (x + y)$.

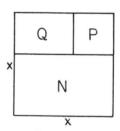

Figure 37G

12

Polygon Constructions

38. Triangle

Fold any three nonparallel creases which will intersect on the sheet.

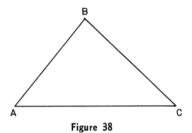

Figure 38

39. Rectangle

Fold any straight line *AB*. Fold points *A* and *B* upon line *AB* to form *CD* and *EF* ⊥ to *AB*. Fold point *C* upon line *CD* to make *GH* ⊥ to *CD*. Why is *DFHG* a rectangle?

Find by superposition what relationships of lines and angles are true for all rectangles.

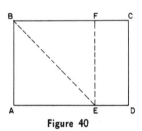

Figure 39

40. Square

Fold the rectangular sheet so that one of the right angles is bisected (line *BE*). Fold *FE* perpendicular to *AD*. Why is *ABFE* a square?

What relationships of lines and angles are true for all squares?

41. Other relationships in the square can be derived by these folds

(a) Fold the diagonals *AC* and *BD* and the medians *EG* and *FH*.
1. How do the diagonals compare in length?
2. At what angles do the diagonals intersect?
3. What triangles formed are congruent?
4. How many triangles are formed?

(b) Fold the creases connecting the midpoints of the sides of the square *EF*, *FG*, *GH*, and *HE*.
1. How does the inscribed square *EFGH* compare with the original square *ABCD*?
2. What triangles formed in this figure are congruent?

Figure 40

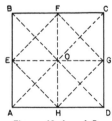

Figure-41 A and B

13

(c) If the area of the original square *ABCD* is 1 square foot, what are the areas of the other squares formed by folding the corners to the center (Figure 41C)?

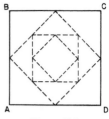

Figure 41C

42. Equilateral triangle

(a) Bisect a rectangular piece of paper *ABCD* by folding one long edge on the other long edge (Figure 42A).

(b) Fold one corner *A* upon *EF* so that the crease *GB* will pass through *B* (Figure 42B).

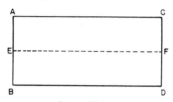

Figure 42A

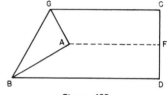

Figure 42B

(c) Fold the corner *B* so that *BG* falls upon the edge *CG* (Figure 42C). Why is *BGH* an equilateral triangle?

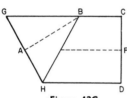

Figure 42C

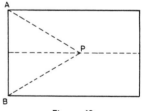

Figure 43

43. Isosceles triangle

Fold the perpendicular bisector of a side *AB* of a rectangular sheet of paper. Fold creases from *A* and *B* to any point *P* on the perpendicular bisector of *AB*.

What angles and lines are equal in this figure?

44. Hexagon

(a) Fold a square *ABCD* to obtain lines *EG* and *FH* which divide the square into four equal parts (Figure 44A).

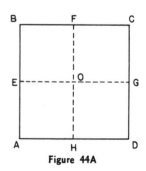

Figure 44A

(b) Locate points *I, J, K, L,* by folding equilateral triangles on *EOI, GOJ, EOL,* and *GOK.*

(c) Fold the hexagon *EIJGKL* (Figure 44C).

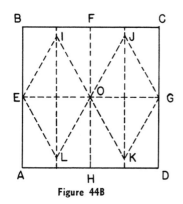

Figure 44B

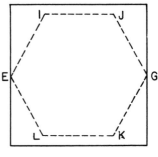

Figure 44C

(d) An easier way to fold a hexagon is to fold the three corners of an equilateral triangle to its center (Figure 44D). How does the area of the triangle *ABC* compare with that of the hexagon *DEFGHI*?

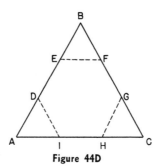

Figure 44D

45. Octagon

Fold a square *ABCD* to obtain the midpoints *E, F, G, H.* Fold the inscribed square *EFGH.* Bisect the angles formed by the sides of the original square and the sides of the inscribed square *EFGH.* Why is *EJFKGLHI* a regular octagon?

By bisecting or trisecting the angles at the centers of squares or triangles, many other polygons can be formed.

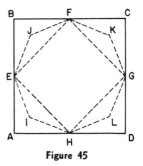

Figure 45

15

Polygons Constructed by Tying Paper Knots

46. Square

Use two strips of paper of the same width.

(a) Fold each strip over upon itself to form a loop (Figure 46A).

(b) Insert an end of one strip into the loop of the other so that the strips interlock. Pull tightly together and cut off surplus. Why is the polygon a square?

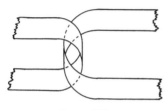

Figure 46A

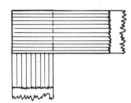

Figure 46B

47. Pentagon

Use a long strip of paper of constant width. Adding machine tape is a convenient size strip to use. Tie an overhand knot like the first knot in tying a shoe string (Figure 47A). Tighten and crease flat. Cut the surplus lengths. Unfold and consider the set of trapezoids formed by the creases. How do the trapezoids compare?

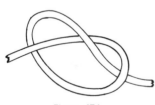

Figure 47A

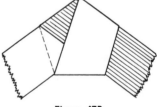

Figure 47B

48. Hexagon

Use two long strips of paper of equal width. Tie a square knot as shown in Figure 48A. Tuck the ends of each strip into the loop of the other. Tighten and crease flat. Cut the surplus lengths.

Figure 48A

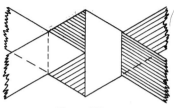

Figure 48B

49. Heptagon

Use a long strip of paper of constant width. Tie a knot like that for the pentagon above but before tightening, pass the lead strip under the knot and back through the center.

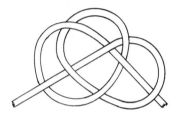

Figure 49A

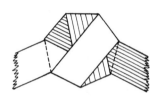

Figure 49B

50. Octagon

Use two long strips of paper of the same width. First tie a loose overhand knot with one strip like that for the pentagon above. The figure below shows this tie with the shaded strip going from 1-2-3-4-5. With the second strip, start at 6, pass over 1-2 and over 3-4. Bend up at 7. Pass under 4-5 and 1-2. Bend up at 9. Pass over 3-4, under 7-8 and 4-5, emerging at 10. Tighten and crease flat. Cut surplus lengths 1, 5, 6, 10.

Figure 50A

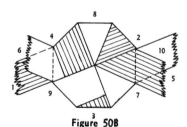

Figure 50B

Symmetry

51. Line symmetry

Fold two perpendicular creases, keeping the paper folded. Cut any edge into a plane curve with scissors. When unfolded, the cut curve is symmetrical to both creases.

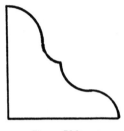

Figure 51A

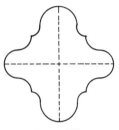

Figure 51B

52. Line and point symmetry

Fold two perpendicular creases, dividing the paper into quadrants. Keep the paper folded. Form a design or geometric figure by pricking through the four layers of paper with a pin. Prick the paper at the vertices of the figure. When the paper is unfolded, the figures formed by the pin pricks will possess line symmetry in adjoining quadrants and point symmetry in alternate quadrants.

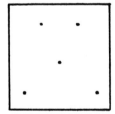

Figure 52A

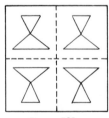

Figure 52B

53. Symmetrical design

Fold two perpendicular creases, dividing the paper into quadrants. Fold once more bisecting the folded right angles. Keep the paper folded. Trim the edge opposite the 45° angle so that all folded parts are equal. While the paper remains folded, cut odd-shaped notches and holes. Be sure to leave parts of the edges intact. When the paper is unfolded, a symmetrical design is apparent.

18

Figure 53A   **Figure 53B**

54. Snowflake pattern

Snowflake patterns can be formed by folding and cutting in much the same way as in Figure 53. A straight angle is formed by a crease. This straight angle can be trisected approximately by folding up both edges of the crease and sliding them between thumbs and fingers until the edges match (Figure 54A). Fold once more to bisect the 60° angles (Figure 54B). Trim and cut many notches as in Figure 54C.

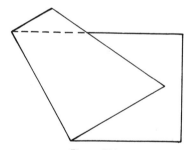

Figure 54A

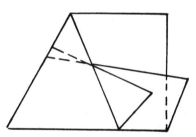

Figure 54B

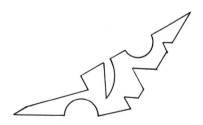

Figure 54C

Conic Sections

55. Parabola

Draw any straight line m to be a directrix. Locate a point F not on the given line to be the focus. Fold the point F upon the directrix m. Repeat this fold from 20 to 30 times by moving F along the line m and creasing. These creases are all tangent to the parabola having F as a focus and the given line as a directrix. These tangents are said to "envelope" the curve and give the illusion of curvature. The result is based on the property that any tangent to a parabola bisects the angle between the focal radius and the line from the point of tangency perpendicular to the directrix.

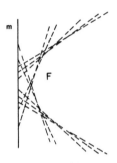

Figure 55

56. Ellipse

Draw a circle with center O. Locate a point F inside the circle. Fold the point F upon the circle. Repeat this fold from 20 to 30 times by moving F along the circle and creasing. Each crease is tangent to an ellipse with foci F and O. The figure at right shows F folded upon X. Since the fold YZ is the perpendicular bisector of FX, $FP = PX$. Thus $OP + FP = OP + PX = OX =$ a constant, the radius. Consequently the locus of P is the ellipse with O and F as foci. The crease YZ is tangent to the ellipse at P since $\angle FPZ = \angle ZPX = \angle OPY$.

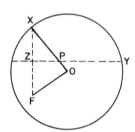

Figure 56

57. Hyperbola

Draw a circle with center O. Locate a point F outside the circle. Fold F upon the circle repeatedly as for the ellipse. Each crease is tangent to the hyperbola having O and F as foci. In the figure at the right F is folded upon X. Since YZ is then the

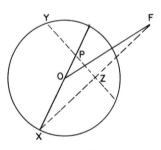

Figure 57

20

perpendicular bisector of FX, $FP = PX$. Thus $FP - PO = PX - PO =$ a constant, the radius. Also $\angle FPZ = \angle XPZ$. The asymptotes are the creases determined by points X that are intersections of the given circle and the circle on OF as a diameter.

58. Conic section models

Form a cone by cutting a sector of a circle (Figure 58A) and gluing along the radii (Figure 58B). Graph the equation $x^2 + y^2 = 144$ and cut out the circle. Place the cut-out circle on the cone to illustrate that a circle is a section of a cone cut by a plane parallel to the base.

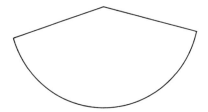

Figure 58A

Figure 58B

Similarly graph an equation such as $x^2 + 4y^2 = 144$ or $x^2 + 25y^2 = 400$. Cut out the ellipse as shown in Figure 58C. Place the ellipse on the cone as shown in Figure 58D to show that an ellipse is a section of a cone.

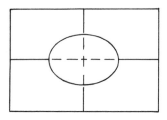

Figure 58C

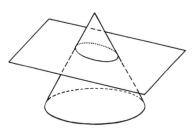

Figure 58D

Draw the graph of $y^2 = 4x$ or $y^2 = 3x$. Mount the graph on cardboard and cut out the concave area as shown in Figure 58E. A simple frame for the parabola can be made by punching holes in the corners of the card with a paper punch and inserting small, rolled-up pieces of paper to serve as legs (Figure 58F). Lay the cone on one side and adjust the graph so that it is parallel to the plane at the table and at a height so that the cone will fit the graph (Figure 58G).

21

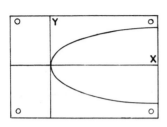

Figure 58E

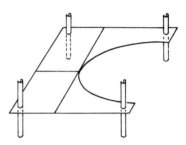

Figure 58F

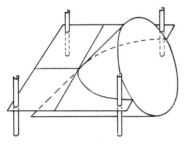

Figure 58G

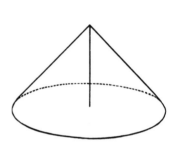

Figure 58H

Graph an equation of the form $y^2 - x^2 = a^2$ or $y^2 - x^2 = 144$. Mount the graph on cardboard and cut out one branch of the resulting hyperbola. Form a cone from a sector having a central angle of $255°$. Under these conditions the asymptotes of the curve will be perpendicular and a section through the axis of the cone (when $a = 0$) should be two perpendicular lines. The axis of the cone and the plane of the curve must be parallel to effect any hyperbolic section. Attach paper feet to the graph (Figure 58I). Fit the graph to the cone in a vertical position as shown in Figure 58J.

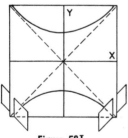

Figure 58I

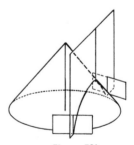

Figure 58J

Recreations

59. Moebius strip

Use a strip of paper at least 1½ inches wide and 24 inches long. If you glue the ends of this strip together, the result is an ordinary round band. To make a Moebius strip, give one end a half turn (180°) before gluing it to the other end. If you draw an unbroken pencil mark on the strip, you will return to the starting point without crossing an edge. Thus this strip of paper has only one surface. Stick the point of a scissors into the center of the paper and cut all the way around. You will be surprised by the result! Cut the resulting band down the middle for a different result. Make another Moebius strip and cut the strip by cutting along the edge ⅓ of the width of the strip from an edge.

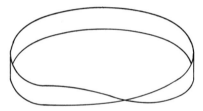

Figure 59

60. Five-point star

Use a five-inch square of paper and fold it from corner to corner (Figure 60A). The base line *AB* will be about seven inches long. Locate *D*, the midpoint of *AB*, by folding *A* on *B*. Locate *E* so that *AE* is ⅓ *AC*. This can be done by folding or by measuring to make *AE* 1-11/16 inches.

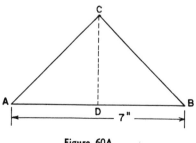

Figure 60A

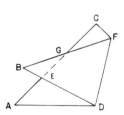

Figure 60B

Fold B over AC so that BD coincides with E (Figure 60B) and BF intersects AC at G. Fold DF upon DB forming a crease DG (Figure 60C).

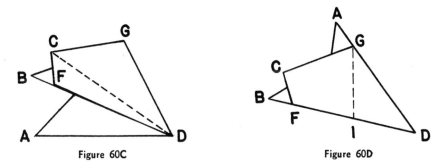

Figure 60C   Figure 60D

Fold AD back and crease along BD so that AD will coincide with GD (Figure 60D). Locate the midpoint I of FD. Cut along the line GI to form the star shown in Figure 60E.

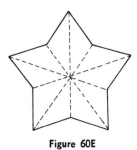

Figure 60E

61. Hexaflexagons

This dramatic variation of the Moebius strip requires a paper strip that is at least six times its width in length.

(a) First fold the strip to locate the center line CD (Figure 61A) at one end of the strip.

(b) Fold the strip so that B falls on CD and the resulting crease AE passes through A (Figure 61B). What kind of a triangle is ABE?

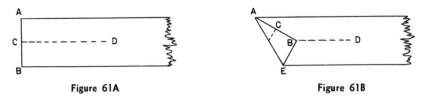

Figure 61A   Figure 61B

24

(c) Fold the strip back so that the crease (*EG*) forms along *BE* (Figure 61C). What kind of a triangle is *EGA*? Next fold forward along *GA*, forming another triangle. Continue folding back and forth until ten equilateral triangles have been formed. Cut off the excess of the strip as well as the first right triangle *ABE*.

(d) Lay the strip in the position shown in Figure 61D and number the triangles accordingly.

(e) Turn the strip over and number as shown in Figure 61E. Be sure that triangle 11 is behind triangle 1. Coloring each triangle or drawing designs on them will add to the attractiveness of the hexaflexagons.

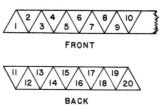

FRONT

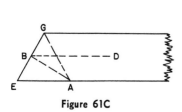

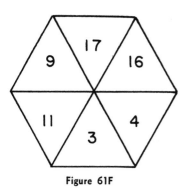

Figure 61C

BACK

Figure 61 D and E

(f) To fold the hexaflexagon, hold the strip in the position shown in Figure 61D. Fold triangle 1 over triangle 2. Then fold triangle 15 on triangle 14 and triangle 8 on triangle 7. If your folding now gives you the arrangements shown in Figures 61F and 61G, glue triangle 1 to 10. If you do not have this arrangement, recheck the directions given.

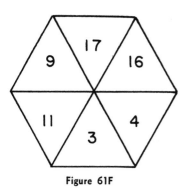

Figure 61F

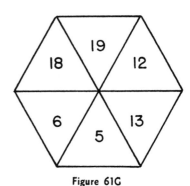

Figure 61G

Your hexagon will now open and give you three surfaces or six designs. The designs open easily by folding in the three single edges, forming a three-cornered star and opening out the center. The *Mathematics Teacher* of April 1951, page 248, gives further directions for folding a hexahexaflexagon which has six surfaces and twelve designs.

62. Pyramid puzzle

Draw the pattern shown in Figure 62 on heavy paper such as manila paper. The triangles, hexagon, and square all have equal length sides. Cut out and fold on the dotted lines. Fasten the edges with cellophane tape. Arrange two of these objects to form a tetrahedron. What unusual cross-section of a tetrahedron is involved?

63. Proof of the fallacy that every triangle is isosceles

Fold the bisector of the vertex angle and the perpendicular bisector of the base. These creases will intersect outside the triangle, which contradicts the assumption that these lines meet inside the circle.

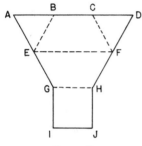

Figure 62

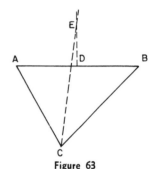

Figure 63

64. Cube

(a) Fold a piece of paper down so as to form a square and remove the excess strip. The edge of the resulting cube will be ¼ the side of the square (Figure 64A).

(b) Fold the paper from corner to corner and across the center one way through the midpoint of the sides (Figure 64B). The fold across the center should be in the opposite direction to that of the corner-to-corner folds.

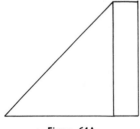

Figure 64A

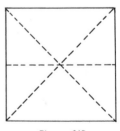

Figure 64B

26

(c) Let the paper fold naturally into shape shown in Figure 64C.
(d) Fold the front A and B (Figure 64D) down to point C.

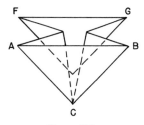

Figure 64C

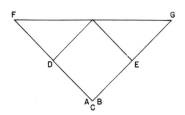

Figure 64D

(e) Turn it over and do the same for the back corners, F and G. A smaller square results (Figure 64E).

(f) The corners on the sides D and E are now double. Fold the corners D and E so that they meet in the center. Turn the square over and do the same for the corners on the back side (Figure 64F).

(g) One end of the Figure 64F will now be free of loose corners. Fold the loose corners on the opposite end H and K outward on the front to form Figure 64G. Do this for the corresponding corners on the back.

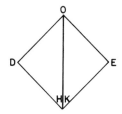

Figure 64E

Figure 64F

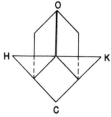

Figure 64G

(h) Fold the points H and K inward to the center. Do the same with the points on the back of the form (Figure 64H).

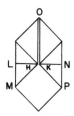

Figure 64H

27

(i) Open out the folds *D* and *E* and tuck the triangles *LHM* and *KNP* into the pockets in *D* and *E*. Do the same with the points on the back (Figure 64I).

(j) Blow sharply into the small hole found at *O* and the cube will inflate. Crease the edges and the cube is finished (Figure 64J).

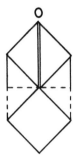

Figure 64I

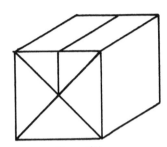

Figure 64J

65. A model of a sphere

Cut three equal circles out of heavy paper. Cut along the lines as shown in Figures 65A, 65B, and 65C. Bend the sides of Figure 65A toward each other along the dotted lines *AB* and *CD* and pass this piece through the cut in the center of Figure 65B. Open Figure 65A after it has been pushed through Figure 65B.

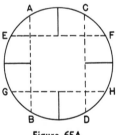

Figure 65A

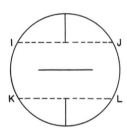

Figure 65B

Bend the sides of Figure 65A along the dotted lines *EF* and *GH* and bend Figure 65B along the dotted lines *IJ* and *KL*. Pass Figures 65A and 65B through the cross-shaped cut in Figure 65C. This will form the sphere model shown in Figure 65D. This model is suitable for demonstrating latitude and longitude, time zones, and spherical triangles. It can also be used as geometric decorations for the Christmas tree or for mobiles. If the model is to be made out of cardboard, Figures 65A and 65C should be cut into two semicircles and fitted into Figure 65B.

28

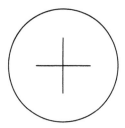

Figure 65C

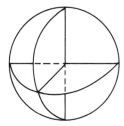

Figure 65D

66. Pop-up dodecahedron

Cut two patterns as shown in Figure 66A out of cardboard. Fold lightly along the dotted lines. Place these patterns together as shown in Figure 66B and attach with a rubber binder. Toss the model into the air and it will form a dodecahedron. If you are not successful in the first attempt, change the rubber binder or use a different type of cardboard.

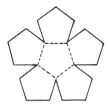

Figure 66A

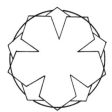

Figure 66B

67. A three-dimensional paper star

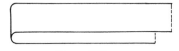

Figure 67A

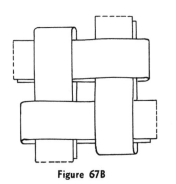

Figure 67B

(a) To make a four-inch star, cut accurately four strips of paper one inch wide and 28 inches long. Use colored paper, plain silver or gold or many-colored Christmas wrappings. If the paper is colored on one side only, cut twice as wide and fold evenly down the length so that color is on both sides. Fold strips in the middle as shown in Figure 67A. Trim ends to form blunt points. Cut strips wider and longer to make larger stars.

(b) Place four folded strips in interlocking position to form a basket weave. Dotted lines in the drawings indicate the continuation of strips throughout these instructions.

(c) Tighten the basket weave until the four strips are firmly interlocked. Turn over. Holding in left hand, turn down front strip at upper left. Crease and turn star clockwise.

(d) Fold down three remaining top strips to form a second basket weave, turning clockwise. When you turn down the fourth strip, weave it through the first strip as shown here.

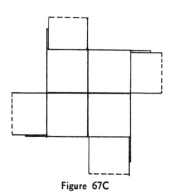

Figure 67C

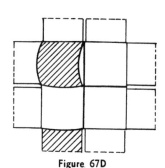

Figure 67D

(e) Fold upper right strip away from you to make right angle triangle #1. Fold strip toward you to form triangle #2. Fold triangle #2 over #1 to form flat point as in Figure 67F.

(f) Fold triangle #3 back and weave the end down through the basket weave as shown. Turn clockwise and make points on three remaining upper righthand strips. Push loose strip out of your way for last weaving.

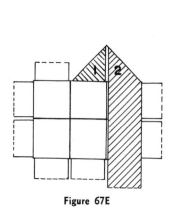

Figure 67E

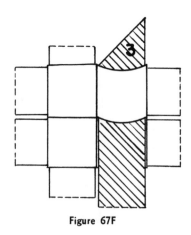

Figure 67F

(g) Turn star over and repeat steps (*d*) and (*e*) until you have eight points. Your star will then look like this—four strips showing back of four points and four strips covering four points (Figure 67G).

(h) To make center points, take end of lower righthand strip in right hand and with a loop motion, keeping right side up, push through upper lefthand basket and flat point.

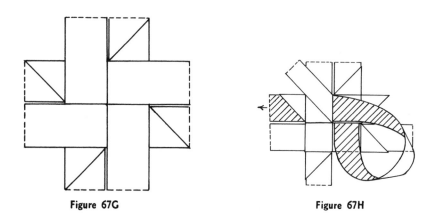

Figure 67G   Figure 67H

(i) Fold lower right strip up, then over to right. Pull strip tight to form point. Turn star clockwise and continue until you have four points at the center. Turn over and repeat on other side. Trim ends.

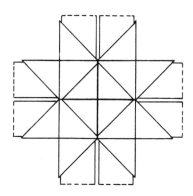

Figure 67I

Patterns for Polyhedrons

Cut the following patterns from cardboard. Fold along the dotted lines. Use the tabs for gluing.

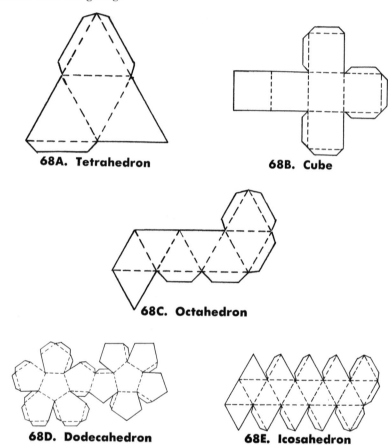

68A. Tetrahedron

68B. Cube

68C. Octahedron

68D. Dodecahedron

68E. Icosahedron

Stellated polyhedrons can be made by attaching pyramids to each face of these regular polyhedrons. Each pyramid should have a base congruent to the face of the polyhedron.